Level 5

Re-told by: Kathryn Harper
Series Editor: Rachel Wilson

Contents

In This Book

Hiro

A 14-year-old boy who builds robots

Tadashi

Hiro's big brother who made Baymax

Baymax

A nurse robot who helps people

Fred, Go Go Tomago, Honey Lemon and Wasabi No-Ginger

Hiro and Tadashi's friends at the lab

Professor Callaghan

A scientist and teacher at the college

Mr. Krei

A businessman who is interested in technology

Before You Read

Introduction

Hiro makes really cool robots. Then he takes them to robot fights and wins money. But sometimes the fights get dangerous and Hiro's brother, Tadashi, has to save him. Since their parents died, Tadashi helps take care of Hiro, but he worries about him. Tadashi shows Hiro that studying at his lab can be fun. But then things get out of control ...

· ·

Activities

1 **Look at the cover and describe what you see. What do you think this story is about?**

> the future   the past   the present   animals   science
> robots   a funny story   an adventure story   a sad story

2 **What do you know about these things? Choose the correct word to complete each sentence.**

> screen   explosion   chip   nurse   college

1 You look at a .... when you use a computer or watch a movie.

2 A .... helps people who are sick.

3 You can find a .... in a computer or robot.

4 A .... is a school for older students.

5 An .... makes a loud noise.

1   Hiro and his Brother

"Can I try?" asked the boy.

"What's your name?" said Yama.

"Hiro," the boy answered.

They put the robots in the circle. "Megabot, destroy!" said Hiro. Megabot broke into pieces and attacked Yama's big robot. It pulled off the arms, then the head. Hiro won but Yama was very angry.

Yama said to his men: "Get him!" Yama's big men ran toward Hiro, but Tadashi arrived at that second. *SCREECH!*

"Hiro, get on!" he cried.

"Are you okay?" Tadashi asked.

"Yes," said Hiro.

"Are you hurt?" asked Tadashi.

"No," said Hiro.

"Then *what* are you *doing*?!" asked Tadashi angrily.

Hiro laughed but Tadashi didn't. Their parents died when Hiro was three. Since then, Tadashi was more than a big brother. They lived with their aunt, but Tadashi also looked after Hiro.

"You're so smart … when are you going to use that mind of yours for something interesting?" asked Tadashi. He wanted Hiro to study at the San Fransokyo Institute of Technology.

Tadashi showed Hiro his lab at the Institute. It was very cool—he loved everything about it.

Hiro met Tadashi's friends. "Welcome to the lab," said Go Go Tamago.

"Hello, Hiro. Are you ready to be surprised?" said Wasabi No-Ginger. He threw an apple in the air and it became paper-thin pieces.

"You must be Hiro!" said Honey Lemon. She smiled.

Hiro met the last friend, Fred. "I'm not a student," he said. Fred just liked to be around smart people.

They went into Tadashi's lab. Hiro asked about Tadashi's work.
He put some tape on Hiro's arm then pulled it off quickly.

"*Ouuuuch!*" cried Hiro.

Suddenly, a big white robot appeared. "Hello. I am Baymax.
How can I help you?" it asked.

"Baymax is a nurse robot," said Tadashi.

"What's that?" asked Hiro.

"He helps people. I programmed him with this green chip,"
said Tadashi.

"Wow! I want to study here!" said Hiro.

"There's Professor Callaghan," said Tadashi. "Ask him."

2 Hiro and the Microbots

How could Hiro show Professor Callaghan that he was a great student? He had an idea. "I'll make Microbots for the student show!"

Hiro worked hard on the little robots. He built a head control that sent ideas from his mind to the Microbots. They flew in the air, then came together to make things—anything—shapes, walls, bridges …

The day of the show, Hiro was really nervous. But everyone loved the Microbots—they were fantastic!

Mr. Krei spoke to Hiro after the show, "I want your Microbots at Kreitech."

"Don't sell them to Krei!" said Professor Callaghan.

"I'll see you in class," said Professor Callaghan to Hiro as Krei walked away.

Tadashi and Hiro talked outside the science building. "Welcome to college," said Tadashi kindly.

Hiro was excited, "This is the *best* day of my life! I wish Mom and Dad—"

"I know," said Tadashi.

"Thank you," said Hiro. "You believed in me when …"

Suddenly, there was a loud noise!

"Run! *FIRE!!*" The doors of the science building opened. People ran out.

"There's smoke … Oh, no!" said Hiro. "The science building is burning!" Tadashi ran toward the building.

"Tadashi, no!" cried Hiro.

"Professor Callaghan's in there," said Tadashi. "Someone has to help!"

KABOOOOM! There was an explosion. Hiro fell to his knees. "Tadashi?" Hiro said softly. "Tadashi …?"

There was no Tadashi. There was only his hat …

3 The Man in the Mask

Tadashi died in the explosion. After that, Hiro just stayed in his bedroom. Day after day. Sometimes he played with Megabot. Until he dropped it on his toe …

"Ouch!" he cried.

Suddenly, Baymax appeared. "Hello, I am Baymax. How can I help you?"

"You're here!" said Hiro.

"Where does it hurt?" asked Baymax.

"I'm fine," said Hiro.

"Are you happy with my help?" asked Baymax.

"What?" asked Hiro.

"I can only turn off if you are happy with my help," said Baymax.

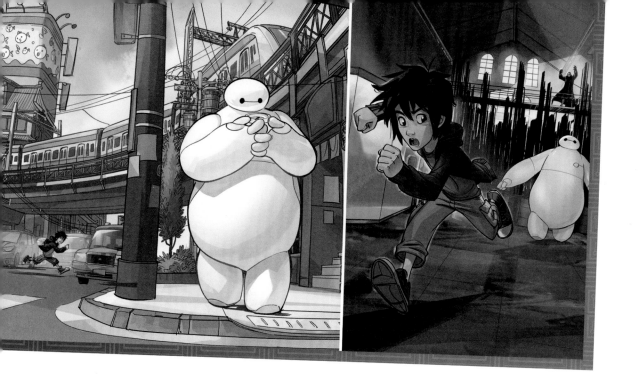

Then Hiro found a Microbot on the bedroom floor, "I don't understand—the fire destroyed them … "

"It's trying to go somewhere," Baymax said. He took the Microbot and left.

"Baymax?" Hiro ran after him.

Hiro found Baymax at an old factory. "It's pointing here," said Baymax. They climbed through a window and saw a machine.

"My Microbots?" said Hiro. "Someone's making more …"

The Microbots suddenly attacked Hiro and Baymax. Then they saw a man in a mask. "He's using my control. It's in his mask," thought Hiro.

"Run!" shouted Hiro.

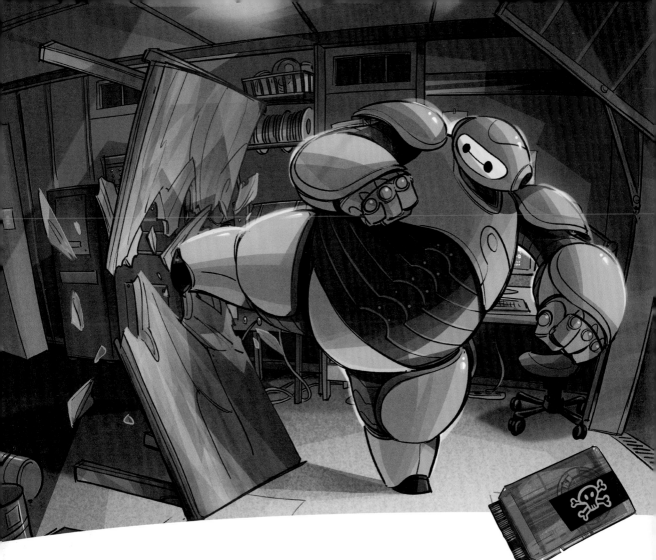

Baymax and Hiro were safe, but Hiro was worried.
The man in the mask stole his Microbots. Did he also make the
explosion? Did his brother die because of that man?

Hiro looked at Baymax. "We're going to catch that man,"
he said. "But first we're going to do some work."

Hiro made a red, fighting chip that he put in Baymax, beside the
green, nurse chip. He also made armor for Baymax. Then the robot
practiced fighting.

Baymax and Hiro went back to the factory, but it was empty. "Your robot is trying to go somewhere," said Baymax. It pointed to the water near the factory.

The masked man was on a mountain of moving Microbots. A car stopped beside Hiro. His friends were in it. Go Go pulled him in.

Suddenly, the masked man was behind the car. Honey took a photo. The man and the Microbots followed them until they crashed into the water. Baymax saved them.

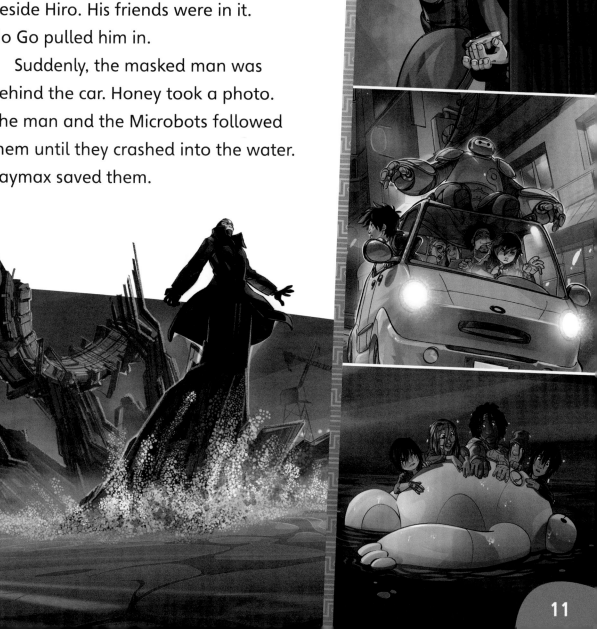

4 Superheroes

Hiro and his friends were back at Fred's house. They were wet and cold. Hiro wanted to catch the man in the mask.

"Catch him? We don't know who he is," said Go Go.

"We want to help but we're just … *us*," said Honey Lemon.

"No," said Hiro. "You can be *much* more …"

"Tadashi was our best friend," said Go Go. "We're in."

"We're going to be Superheroes!" cried Fred.

special bag

new armor; rocket arm

special gloves

special disks

jumping clothes

Hiro put on his new black and purple Superhero clothes.
He smiled. He felt like a Superhero. He and Baymax practiced flying.
Soon, they were ready to find the man in the mask.

Baymax looked at his screen. *Blip, blip, blip, blip, BEEP!*
"There's something on that island," he said.

Baymax flew from the city with Hiro and his friends. "There,"
said Hiro. He pointed to a building on the island. "Baymax, take
us in."

On the island, they found an old lab, but it was empty. When they looked around, they found a video. It showed Mr. Krei in that lab, and a portal. Then the video showed a pilot called Abigail. She was in a space pod.

The space pod went into the portal—but something terrible happened. After Abigail's pod went through the portal, there was an explosion! They shut down the portal.

"Krei is the man is the mask," said Hiro.

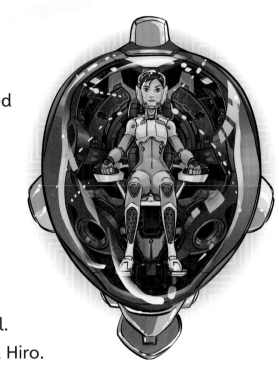

3:21:46

LAB CAMERA 03

The man in the mask and the Microbots were outside the lab.
They attacked, but the Superheroes fought back.

"The control's in the mask," shouted Hiro.

They fought. Finally, Hiro hit the man and his mask fell off.
But it wasn't Krei … It was Professor Callaghan!

"The explosion," said Hiro. "You died."

"No," said Professor Callaghan. "I had your Microbots."

"But Tadashi," said Hiro. "He went in there to save you."

"That was his mistake!" said Professor Callaghan coldly.

Hiro was very, very angry. He pointed to Professor Callaghan and shouted: "Baymax, *DESTROY*!" Baymax didn't move.

"I am a nurse robot. I help people," said Baymax. Hiro took out the green, nurse chip from Baymax. Suddenly, Baymax changed. His rocket arm pointed at Professor Callaghan.

"*STOP!*" shouted the friends. Then Honey Lemon put the nurse chip back in Baymax and he stopped. But Professor Callaghan ran away.

Hiro turned to his friends. "Why did you stop Baymax?!" he cried angrily.

5 Learning to Help

Hiro was home with Baymax. He was still very angry. He wanted to take out Baymax's green chip. "Do you want to destroy Professor Callaghan?" Baymax asked. "Is that what Tadashi would want?"

Baymax showed Hiro an old video with Tadashi in it. In the video, Tadashi finished making Baymax and he looked very happy. "You're going to help so many people," said Tadashi to Baymax, in the video. Hiro touched his brother on the screen and cried.

"I'm so sorry, Baymax," he said.

Hiro's friends arrived. "We're going to catch Callaghan," said Go Go. "But this time we'll do it right."

"We found something. Watch this," said Honey Lemon. They watched the video. It showed Professor Callaghan and Mr. Krei in the island lab. They were beside the portal and Callaghan was very angry.

"You did this!" shouted Callaghan. "You knew the portal wasn't ready."

Then they saw that Abigail's last name was Callaghan. She was Professor Callaghan's daughter. He thought she died because of Krei.

Mr. Krei was in front of his beautiful new building.

Suddenly, Professor Callaghan was there in his mask. The Microbots caught Krei. He couldn't move. "You took my daughter from me. Now I'm taking everything from you," said Callaghan.

Quickly, the Microbots put the pieces of a portal together. Then the portal started pulling the building in.

Hiro and his friends arrived. "Stop," said Hiro.

"I'll give you anything," said Krei.

"I want my daughter," said Callaghan.

"Take Callaghan's mask," shouted Hiro. "Then he can't control the Microbots."

The friends tried to get the mask, but Professor Callaghan and the Microbots were too strong and too fast. The portal pulled rocks, Microbots, and parts of the building in. As Hiro almost fell into the portal, he watched the Microbots.

"New plan," said Hiro to his friends. "Forget the mask. We'll break up the Microbots, then the portal will pull them in."

Honey and Fred made smoke so Callaghan couldn't see.

Hiro flew with Baymax. "Ready?" he said. They flew into the big Microbot shapes and they broke into little pieces. Hiro and his friends worked together, and the portal pulled in the single Microbots.

"This stops now!" shouted Callaghan but nothing happened.

"Looks like you don't have enough Microbots," said Hiro. Most of the Microbots were in the portal.

Baymax got near to Professor Callaghan. He took his mask, then all the other Microbots flew into the portal. Professor Callaghan had no mask. He had no Microbots. He had no power. The portal crashed to the ground.

6 Abigail

The portal was on the ground but it was still working. "We must turn off the portal," said Hiro.

"We can't," said Krei.

Everyone ran away … except Baymax. He didn't move. "There is life in there," said Baymax, pointing to the portal. "Female … in a deep sleep."

"Callaghan's daughter?" asked Hiro. "She didn't die?"

"Abigail …" said Callaghan.

Hiro jumped on Baymax. "Let's go get her," he said.

"It's too dangerous," said Krei.

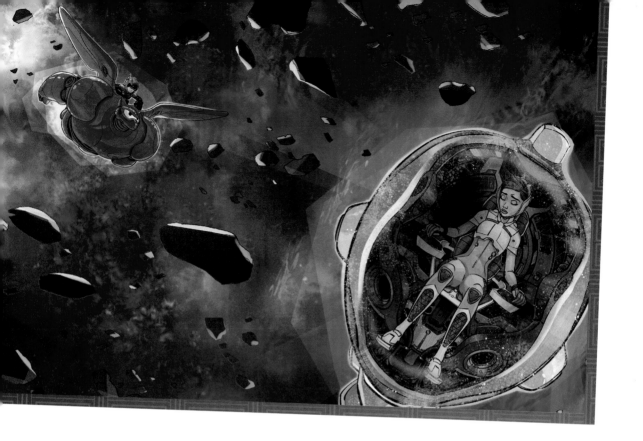

"Someone has to help," said Hiro.

Baymax and Hiro flew into the portal.

"Careful!" cried Hiro. Baymax moved around the flying rocks and other things.

"The person is there," said Baymax. He pointed to a pod.

"Come on," said Hiro. They flew to the pod and Hiro could see Abigal in it. "Let's get her home," said Hiro.

Hiro held on to the pod while Baymax flew them toward the portal door. There were large rocks everywhere.

"Nearly there!" shouted Hiro.

Suddenly, a large rock flew toward him. Baymax moved so the rock hit him, not Hiro. *Thud!* Most of Baymax's armor flew away.

"Baymax!" shouted Hiro. He took his hand.

"There is a way I can get you home," said Baymax. He put his robot arm on the space pod.

"No!" cried Hiro. "I won't leave you here!"

"There is no time," said Baymax.

"Are you happy with my help?" asked Baymax.

"Please, no ... I can't lose you, too," said Hiro.

"I will always be with you," said Baymax. "Are you happy with my help?"

Hiro held Baymax one last time. "I am happy with your help," said Hiro sadly.

Whoosh! Baymax's robot arm pushed Hiro and the pod toward the portal door. Hiro looked back and saw Baymax—he was smaller and smaller. Then Hiro and Abigail crashed through the portal door.

Hiro and the pod fell to the ground.

"They made it!" cried Fred. The friends ran to Hiro and the pod, but then … they understood.

"Baymax?" asked Wasabi. Hiro was so sad that he couldn't speak. He turned to Abigail. She was safe.

"Abigail, you're going to be fine," said a nurse, and they took her to the hospital. The police officers put Professor Callaghan in a police car. Hiro and his friends watched them drive away.

7 Big Hero 6

On the news, people heard about some Superheroes, but they didn't know who they were.

Hiro started classes at the Institute of Technology with his friends. He began to feel better.

In his brother's old lab, Hiro took Baymax's robot arm out of a box. Then he saw something green in the hand. When he opened the fingers, he found Baymax's green, nurse chip! There was a big smile on Hiro's face … he could build a new Baymax with this!

Soon, Hiro heard the words: "Hello, I am Baymax. How can I help you?" Hiro's old friend was back and he felt so happy.

Hiro and his friends Wasabi, Honey Lemon, Go Go Tamago, Fred, and Baymax were ready.

"We didn't plan to be Superheroes. But sometimes life doesn't go the way you planned," said Hiro. "The good thing is, my brother wanted to help a lot of people. And that's what we are going to do. Who are we?"

They were **Big Hero 6!**

After You Read

1 **Who says these things? Read and say.**

Hiro   Tadashi   Professor Callaghan   Baymax   Go Go Tamago

1 Professor Callaghan's in there! Someone has to help!

2 Are you happy with my help?

3 I want my daughter!

4 We're going to catch Callaghan. But this time we'll do it right.

5 I can't lose you, too.

2 **What does Hiro learn in the story? Match and say.**

Can you think of more examples?

1 He learns to understand his sadness.

2 He learns to help and not destroy.

3 He understands why friends are important.

4 He learns to work hard.

a He doesn't hurt Krei.

b He asks his friends to be Superheroes.

c He makes the Microbots.

d Baymax dies.

3 **Why do these things happen? Complete the sentences.**

1 Hiro wants to go to college because …

2 Tadashi goes into the fire because …

3 The friends become Superheroes because …

4 Baymax and Hiro go into the portal because …

Glossary

armor (*noun*) metal clothes that keep people safe

attack past tense **attacked** (*verb*) to try and hurt or kill people; *Megabot broke into pieces and attacked Yama's big robot.*

chip (*noun*) a small part in computers

control (*noun*) something you use to make a machine work

crash past tense **crashed** (*verb*) to hit something very fast and dangerously; *Then Hiro and Abigail crashed through the portal door.*

destroy past tense **destroyed** (*verb*) to break something badly so you can't use it; *I don't understand—the fire destroyed them …*

disk (*noun*) a small piece of plastic or metal that keeps information from a computer

empty (*adj.*) having nothing inside; *Baymax and Hiro went back to the factory, but it was empty.*

explosion (*noun*) an explosion destroys things and makes a big noise and fire

lab (**laboratory**) (*noun*) a room or building where scientists work

machine (*noun*) a thing that engineers build to do a job more quickly then people can

mask (*noun*) something that covers your face; *The man in the mask stole his Microbots.*

mind (*noun*) in your head, what you think

portal (*noun*) a door or entrance to something

program past tense **programmed** (*verb*) to tell a computer to do a job; *I programmed him with this green chip.*

safe (*adj.*) not in danger; *Baymax and Hiro were safe.*

screen (*noun*) glass part of computer or television where you see pictures

smoke (*noun*) white, gray, or black clouds that come from fire

space pod (*noun*) small part of spaceship—you can sit inside a pod

video (*noun*) a copy of a movie or television program

Play: Flying over San Fransokyo

Scene 1:

It's the end of the day in San Fransokyo. The sky is beautiful.

HIRO: [looking at the city] I love the lights of San Fransokyo.

BAYMAX: It is a beautiful evening.

HIRO: Let's fly, Baymax.

BAYMAX: [putting on his armor] Okay. I'm ready.

Scene 2:

Hiro and Baymax fly over San Fransokyo.

HIRO: [on Baymax] This is cool! Go higher, Baymax.

BAYMAX: We are near the clouds.

HIRO: Wow! Look at the buildings. The lights.

BAYMAX: What are those round things? I am flying closer …

HIRO: They're wind turbines. Let's go to one.

Scene 3:

Hiro and Baymax stand on a wind turbine.

HIRO: Whoa!

BAYMAX: Hold on to me.

HIRO: The turbine's making electricity.

BAYMAX: Oh, yes. All the lights need electricity.

HIRO: … I do love those lights!

Global Citizenship

Rooftop Gardens Bring Green to the City

Big cities are busy, and there's not much green space. But there are spaces in cities where there's nothing. Can you guess where? The tops of tall buildings!

In Hong Kong, Rooftop Republic is changing rooftops into gardens. They plan and build gardens, and teach people to grow food on the top of buildings.

There are many great things about rooftop gardens. Growing food in the city means that planes and trucks don't need to bring it in. People can get fresh food where they live. The gardens keep the buildings warmer or cooler. Best of all, the gardens are a great place to enjoy nature in the city!

Rooftop Republic has 61 city farms in Hong Kong.

33

How can robots help sick children?

Do you ever have a sick day when you stay home from school? The first day is okay. The second day can be a little boring … But if you're off school for weeks or even months? That's not fun.

Telepresence robots take children back to the classroom. From the hospital, the sick child can control the robot. The robot has a screen, a camera, a microphone, and a speaker. The child can turn the robot to look where they want. Most importantly, the robot has wheels and can move around the classroom and the school.

Gemma's Story

Gemma was in the hospital for many months. She missed her friends and school. Then her school got a telepresence robot. From the hospital, Gemma was in the lessons, listening, answering questions, and doing work with her classmates. At lunch time, she had lunch with her friends. After school, she sang in the music club. This was all with the help of her robot. That's fantastic!

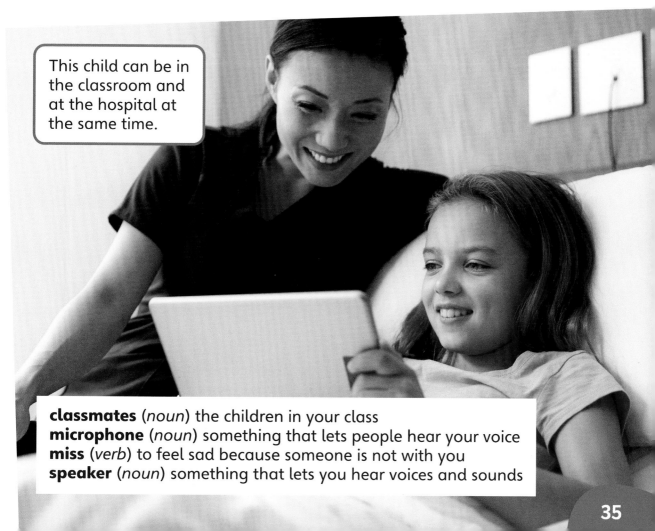

This child can be in the classroom and at the hospital at the same time.

classmates (*noun*) the children in your class
microphone (*noun*) something that lets people hear your voice
miss (*verb*) to feel sad because someone is not with you
speaker (*noun*) something that lets you hear voices and sounds

Phonics

Say the sounds. Read the words.

kn

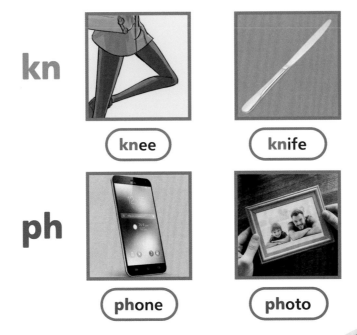

knee

knife

ph

phone

photo

Read, then say the rhyme to a friend.

Hiro saw a dolphin in the San Fransokyo Bay.
He quickly took a photo before it swam away.

Then someone knocked his hand, and his phone fell on the floor.
Was his phone destroyed? He didn't know for sure.

He got down on his knees—Phew! His phone was okay.
And the photo of the dolphin was the best one of the day!